Benchmark and Unit Tests
Teacher's Edition

Grade 6

 **HOUGHTON MIFFLIN HARCOURT**

Contents

Grade 6 Benchmark and Unit Tests
Teacher's Edition

Introduction

As you use the Houghton Mifflin Harcourt *Journeys* instructional program, you have a rich array of materials to foster students' achievement week by week and unit by unit. The assessment materials supplement the *Journeys* program, helping you determine what Common Core State Standards students have mastered and which require additional instruction.

The Weekly Tests and the Periodic Assessments (Fluency Tests and Checklists) show achievement in specific program skill strands throughout a unit. At the *end* of each unit, you can use a Benchmark Test or a Unit Test to obtain a broader picture of achievement. Each unit also has a test called Reading Complex Text. These tests have students read complex text and respond to open-ended questions.

Benchmark Tests The Benchmark Tests are given three times a year, at the end of Units 1, 3, and 5. These tests focus on the key reading/language arts skills that have been taught to date. The Unit 1 Benchmark Test draws upon selected skills from that unit as well as other skills that indicate progress with the Common Core State Standards. The Benchmark Tests in Units 3 and 5 are summative, drawing upon skills that have been taught in the program up to the point of administration along with other indicators of reading progress.

Each Benchmark Test has three sections. The **Reading and Analyzing Text** section assesses comprehension and vocabulary strategies. The **Revising and Editing** section draws upon the grammar, spelling, and writing skills taught to date. The **Writing** section provides a writing prompt, reflecting the modes, forms, and skills taught to date.

Test items and test formats provide essential practice in test-taking strategies. In addition, the Answer Keys correlate the items to appropriate strands in the Teacher's Edition, to help you plan re-teaching lessons and extra practice as needed.

Unit Tests Alternating with the Benchmark Tests, the Unit Tests assess progress on the skills taught in Units 2, 4, and 6. Unlike the Benchmark Tests, the Unit Tests are not cumulative but provide a focus on the skills in a particular unit. The results help you to confirm scores on the Weekly Tests and to pinpoint Common Core State Standards for re-teaching or challenge lessons. The Unit Test sections **(Reading and Analyzing Text, Revising and Editing, Writing)** and item formats also provide practice with test-taking strategies, and the Answer Keys correlate the items to instructional lessons in the program.

Novel Tests In addition to the Unit Test provided for the skills reviewed in Unit 6, a Novel Test is included for each literature option in that unit. Use the appropriate Novel Test to match each student's assignment and assess comprehension.

Reading Complex Text After each Benchmark Test or Unit Test is a test of Reading Complex Text. These tests use text-embedded questions to assess students' ability to closely read complex text and provide text-based evidence in response to open-ended questions. The questions are based on the Common Core State Standards taught in the previous and current units. These tests prepare students for the kinds of texts and questions they will encounter on tests of the Common Core State Standards.

Administering the Tests

The tests are group-administered. At Grade 2 and beyond, students can read the directions and take the tests independently. Duplicate copies of the Answer Document from this book and remind students to mark their answers on it. Since there may be more rows than needed for a particular test, help students find out how many items are in each multiple-choice section and draw a line under the last row they will need. For each Benchmark and Unit Test, the sections may be given on different days.

Scoring the Benchmark and Unit Tests

The **Reading and Analyzing Text** and **Revising and Editing** subtests consist of multiple-choice items. Correct the tests using the Answer Keys in this book, placing a check mark next to each correct response on the Answer Document. Each correct response is worth one point. Duplicate a Test Record Form for each student and enter the scores in the Student Score column. This form will allow you to track a student's performance across the year.

If you require a percentage score for each test to help in assigning grades, apply the formula in the optional Percent Correct column and record that score.

For **Writing,** score each student's writing by using the Writing Rubrics in this book and enter the score on the Test Record Form.

Scoring the Reading Complex Text Sections

Use the Answer Keys to score the open-ended items on these tests. The first three items on the test are worth one point each. The last item is worth two points. Sample answers are given on the Answer Key and should be used as a guide to score student's responses. Because these questions require students to think deeply about comprehension, both the teacher and students can learn a great deal by discussing students' responses and their reasoning.

Interpreting the Results

Consider each student's scores on the Test Record Form. Students who achieve an Acceptable Score (indicated on the form) or higher are most likely ready to proceed with the next unit. You may want to look at class scores across each subtest to see if there are specific skills you should reinforce with the whole class in the next unit.

For struggling students, duplicate the Performance Summary. Circle the item numbers answered incorrectly on each Benchmark Test or Unit Test subtest and compare them to the corresponding skills indicated on the Answer Keys. Look for patterns among the errors to help you decide which skills need re-teaching and more practice. To assess progress after re-teaching, re-administer an appropriate Weekly Test or go over errors on the Benchmark or Unit Test and have the student explain which responses are correct. Consider intervention for students who still have a wide array of errors.

Summary

The broad picture of reading/writing achievement offered by the tests in this book helps you in three important ways:

- The tests show you how students combine the skills from the Weekly Tests and apply them to new selections.
- Students' performance helps you tailor your instruction to meet their needs.
- The formats and skills on the tests in this book prepare students with important test-taking strategies.

Use the options in the *Journeys* assessment materials to verify progress and enhance your teaching throughout the year.

Answer Key
Unit 1 Benchmark Test

Item Number	Correct Answer	Unit, Lesson, Program Skill	Common Core State Standard	Webb's Depth of Knowledge*
		READING AND ANALYZING TEXT		
1	C	U1L1: Comprehension: Dialogue	RL.6.3	2
2	G	U1L1: Vocabulary Strategy: Prefixes *dis-, ex-, inter-, non-*	L.6.4b	2
3	C	U1L5: Vocabulary Strategy: Reference Sources	L.6.4c	2
4	G	U1L4: Comprehension: Alliteration	RL.6.4	3
5	D	U1L1: Comprehension: Understanding Characters	RL.6.3	2
6	H	U1L1: Comprehension: Understanding Characters	RL.6.3	1
7	A	U1L2: Comprehension: Author's Purpose	RI.6.6	3
8	I	U1L2: Vocabulary Strategy: Suffixes *-er, -or, -ar, -ist, -ian, -ent*	L.6.4b	2
9	B	U1L3: Vocabulary Strategy: Multiple-Meaning Words	L.6.4d	2
10	F	U1L2: Comprehension: Author's Purpose	RI.6.6	3
11	A	U1L2: Comprehension: Figurative Language	RI.6.4	2
12	I	U1L5: Comprehension: Fact and Opinion	RI.6.8	2
13	C	U1L5: Comprehension: Analyze Events	RI.6.3	3
14	G	U1L5: Comprehension: Author's Purpose	RI.6.6	3
15	B	U1L3: Comprehension: Sequence of Events	RI.6.5	3
16	I	U1L2: Vocabulary Strategy: Suffixes *-er, -or, -ar, -ist, -ian, -ent*	L.6.4b	2
17	C	U1L3: Comprehension: Domain-Specific Vocabulary	RI.6.4	2
18	G	U1L1: Comprehension: Simile	RL.6.4	3
19	A	U1L4: Comprehension: Style and Tone	L.6.3b	3
20	H	U1L4: Comprehension: Story Structure	RL.6.3	2
21	A	U1L4: Comprehension: Story Structure	RL.6.3	2
22	G	U1L4: Vocabulary Strategy: Prefixes *de-, trans-*	L.6.4b	2
23	C	U1L4: Comprehension: Style and Tone	L.6.3b	3
24	I	U1L1: Comprehension: Understanding Characters	RL.6.3	2
25	A	U1L5: Vocabulary Strategy: Reference Sources	L.6.4c	2
26	I	U1L4: Comprehension: Story Structure	RL.6.3	3
27	C	U1L1: Comprehension: Understanding Characters	RL.6.3	1
28	F	U1L1: Comprehension: Dialogue	RL.6.3	2
29	C	U1L4: Comprehension: Style and Tone	L.6.3b	3
30	F	U1L2: Comprehension: Author's Purpose	RI.6.6	3

* Webb's Depth of Knowledge refers to the level of knowledge the item requires of the student. For more information see: Webb, N.L., 1999, Alignment Between Standards and Assessment, University of Wisconsin Center for Educational Research.

Unit 1 Benchmark Test continued

Item Number	Correct Answer	Unit, Lesson, Program Skill	Common Core State Standard	Webb's Depth of Knowledge*
31	C	U1L3: Comprehension: Domain-Specific Vocabulary	RI.6.4	2
32	F	U1L2: Comprehension: Point of View	RI.6.6	2
33	D	U1L4: Vocabulary Strategy: Prefixes de-, trans-	L.6.4b	2
34	G	U1L5: Comprehension: Fact and Opinion	RI.6.8	1
35	D	U1L3: Comprehension: Diagrams	RI.6.7	2
REVISING AND EDITING				
1	B	U1L5: Writing Trait: Word Choice	W.6.5	3
2	H	U1L4: Writing Trait: Organization	W.6.5	3
3	B	U1L5: Spelling: Homophones	L.6.2b	1
4	F	U1L4: Grammar: Common and Proper Nouns	L.4.2a**	1
5	A	U1L3: Grammar: Subjects and Predicates	L.5.3a**	2
6	I	U1L2: Grammar: Kinds of Sentences	L.4.3b**	1
7	C	U1L1: Grammar: Complete Sentences	L.4.1f**	2
8	F	U1L3: Grammar: Subjects and Predicates	L.5.3a**	2
9	A	U1L5: Grammar: Other Kinds of Nouns	L.3.1b**	1
10	I	U1L2: Grammar: Kinds of Sentences	L.4.3b**	1
11	C	U1L4: Grammar: Common and Proper Nouns	L.4.2a**	1
12	I	U1L4: Writing Trait: Organization	W.6.5	3
13	A	U1L1: Grammar: Complete Sentences	L.4.1f**	2
14	G	U1L2: Spelling: Long Vowels	L.6.2b	1
15	D	U1L2: Grammar: Kinds of Sentences	L.4.3b**	1
16	I	U1L5: Grammar: Other Kinds of Nouns	L.3.1b**	1
17	A	U1L5: Grammar: Other Kinds of Nouns	L.3.2d**	1
18	F	U1L3: Grammar: Subjects and Predicates	L.5.3a**	2
19	D	U1L1: Grammar: Complete Sentences	L.4.1f**	2
20	I	U1L5: Writing Trait: Word Choice	W.6.5	3
WRITING TO NARRATE				
See rubric on page 28.		U1L5: Narrative Writing	W.6.3a, W.6.3b, W.6.3c, W.6.3d, W.6.3e	4

** Maintained from previous grade(s).

Unit 1 Reading Complex Text

Item 1		
Scoring Rubric	**0 points**	Student does not respond correctly; no response.
	1 point	Answers may vary. Sample response: The author's focus on competition in the first paragraph contrasts with the second paragraph because the author explains that the trail was once used for teamwork—*not* competition.

Unit, Lesson, Program Skill	Common Core State Standard	Webb's Depth of Knowledge*
U1L3: Comprehension: Sequence of Events	RI.6.5	2

Item 2		
Scoring Rubric	**0 points**	Student does not respond correctly; no response.
	1 point	Answers may vary. Sample responses: Two words or phrases that aid in the understanding of the meaning of the word *epidemic*. Words or phrases may include *disease, diphtheria, threatened the entire population, sickened, stop the disease from spreading,* and *fallen ill*.

Unit, Lesson, Program Skill	Common Core State Standard	Webb's Depth of Knowledge*
U1L3: Comprehension: Domain-Specific Vocabulary	RI.6.4	2

Item 3		
Scoring Rubric	**0 points**	Student does not respond correctly; no response.
	1 point	Answers may vary. Sample response: Balto stepped up and became a lead dog when the previous lead dog was unable to find the trail, leading the team in the final two legs of the relay and delivering the serum to Nome.

Unit, Lesson, Program Skill	Common Core State Standard	Webb's Depth of Knowledge*
U1L5: Comprehension: Analyze Events	RI.6.3	1

Item 4		
Scoring Rubric	**0 points**	Student does not respond correctly; no response.
	1 point	Answers may vary. Student identifies author's purpose in the article but does *not* explain how the author uses the stories of Togo and Balto to help convey this purpose. (See below for sample correct response.)
	2 points	Answers may vary. Sample response: The author's purpose in the article is to inform readers of the journey that partly inspired the Iditarod Trail Sled Dog Race, in which mushers and sled dogs across Alaska came together to help deliver a life-saving serum to the town of Nome. The author uses the stories about two lead dogs, Togo and Balto, to illustrate challenges the teams faced and heroic efforts they made in order to deliver the serum.

Unit, Lesson, Program Skill	Common Core State Standard	Webb's Depth of Knowledge*
U1L5: Comprehension: Author's Purpose	RI.6.6	3

Unit 2 Unit Test

Item Number	Correct Answer	Unit, Lesson, Program Skill	Common Core State Standard	Webb's Depth of Knowledge*
		READING AND ANALYZING TEXT		
1	D	U2L7: Target Vocabulary	L.6.6	1
2	I	U2L7: Vocabulary Strategy: Word Relationships	L.6.5b	2
3	D	U2L7: Decoding: *Schwa* in Unstressed Syllables	RF.5.3a**	1
4	F	U2L6: Target Vocabulary	L.6.6	1
5	C	U2L7: Comprehension: Text Structure	RI.6.5	3
6	F	U2L8: Vocabulary Strategy: Latin Roots and Affixes	L.6.4b	2
7	C	U2L8: Decoding: Common Final Syllables	RF.5.3a**	1
8	F	U2L6: Vocabulary Strategy: Using Context	L.6.4a	2
9	A	U2L10: Comprehension: Author's Purpose	RI.6.6	3
10	F	U2L9: Vocabulary Strategy: Denotation and Connotation	L.6.5c	2
11	B	U2L10: Comprehension: Arguments and Claims	RI.6.8	3
12	H	U2L6: Target Vocabulary	L.6.6	1
13	B	U2L7: Comprehension: Text and Graphic Features	RI.6.7	1
14	I	U2L10: Decoding: Recognizing Common Suffixes	RF.5.3a**	1
15	A	U2L10: Comprehension: Compare and Contrast	RI.6.1	2
16	G	U2L10: Comprehension: Compare and Contrast	RI.6.1	3
17	C	U2L10: Comprehension: Compare and Contrast	RI.6.1	2
18	H	U2L9: Comprehension: Cause and Effect	RL.6.3	1
19	A	U2L9: Target Vocabulary	L.6.6	1
20	G	U2L7: Vocabulary Strategy: Word Relationships	L.6.5b	2
21	B	U2L7: Decoding: *Schwa* in Unstressed Syllables	RF.5.3a**	1
22	I	U2L8: Decoding: Common Final Syllables	RF.5.3a**	1
23	C	U2L6: Decoding: Silent Consonants in Multisyllable Words	RF.5.3a**	1
24	G	U2L9: Comprehension: Cause and Effect	RL.6.3	1
25	B	U2L9: Vocabulary Strategy: Denotation and Connotation	L.6.5c	2
26	G	U2L10: Vocabulary Strategy: Synonyms	L.6.4c	2
27	A	U2L6: Vocabulary Strategy: Using Context	L.6.4a	2
28	H	U2L9: Comprehension: Point of View	RL.6.6	2
29	A	U2L10: Target Vocabulary	L.6.6	1
30	F	U2L6: Decoding: Silent Consonants in Multisyllable Words	RF.5.3a**	1

** Maintained from previous grade(s).

Unit 2 Unit Test continued

Item Number	Correct Answer	Unit, Lesson, Program Skill	Common Core State Standard	Webb's Depth of Knowledge*
31	D	U2L8: Comprehension: Character's Motivations	RL.6.3	1
32	H	U2L9: Comprehension: Style and Tone	RL.6.4	2
33	D	U2L8: Target Vocabulary	L.6.6	1
34	H	U2L6: Comprehension: Theme	RL.6.2	2
35	D	U2L8: Comprehension: Conclusions and Generalizations	RL.6.1	2
		REVISING AND EDITING		
1	D	U2L7: Writing Trait: Organization	W.6.5	3
2	G	U2L6: Grammar: Kinds of Verbs	L.3.1f**	1
3	B	U2L9: Grammar: Subordinating Conjunctions	L.5.3a**	2
4	F	U2L6: Spelling: Words with *ie* or *ei*	L.6.2b	1
5	D	U2L7: Grammar: Verbs and Objects	L.6.1a	1
6	I	U2L10: Grammar: Longer Sentences	L.5.3a**	1
7	C	U2L8: Grammar: Coordinating Conjunctions	L.5.1a**	1
8	I	U2L9: Grammar: Subordinating Conjunctions	L.5.1a**	1
9	C	U2L8: Grammar: Coordinating Conjunctions	L.5.1a**	1
10	H	U2L8: Spelling: Final /ən/, /əl/, and /ər/	L.6.2b	1
11	C	U2L6: Grammar: Kinds of Verbs	L.4.1b**	1
12	G	U2L10: Writing Trait: Sentence Fluency	W.6.5	3
13	A	U2L7: Grammar: Verbs and Objects	L.6.1a	1
14	G	U2L10: Grammar: Longer Sentences	L.5.1a**	1
15	B	U2L7: Writing Trait: Organization	W.6.5	3
16	F	U2L6: Grammar: Kinds of Verbs	L.3.1e**	1
17	C	U2L7: Grammar: Verbs and Objects	L.3.1a**	1
18	G	U2L10: Grammar: Longer Sentences	L.6.3a	3
19	C	U2L8: Grammar: Coordinating Conjunctions	L.5.1a**	1
20	I	U2L10: Spelling: Endings and Suffixes	L.6.2b	1
		WRITING ARGUMENTS		
	See rubric on page 24.	U2L10: Argumentative Writing	W.6.1a, W.6.1b, W.6.1c, W.6.1d, W.6.1e	4

** Maintained from previous grade(s).

Unit 2 Reading Complex Text

Item 1		
Scoring Rubric	**0 points**	Student does not respond correctly; no response.
	1 point	Answers may vary. Sample response: Decomposition is a natural process by which dead plant and animal matter decays, or breaks down.

Unit, Lesson, Program Skill	**Common Core State Standard**	**Webb's Depth of Knowledge***
U1L3: Comprehension: Domain-Specific Vocabulary	RI.6.4	2

Item 2		
Scoring Rubric	**0 points**	Student does not respond correctly; no response.
	1 point	Answers may vary. Sample response: Organic waste (green and brown materials), air, water, and soil are needed to make compost. Heat, carbon dioxide, and compost are produced in the process.

Unit, Lesson, Program Skill	**Common Core State Standard**	**Webb's Depth of Knowledge***
U2L7: Comprehension: Text and Graphic Features	RI.6.7	1

Item 3		
Scoring Rubric	**0 points**	Student does not respond correctly; no response.
	1 point	Answers may vary. Sample response: The author promotes composting by arguing that making compost is easy and by describing its benefits (such as that it takes little time, improves your yard, saves money, preserves natural resources, and protects your health).

Unit, Lesson, Program Skill	**Common Core State Standard**	**Webb's Depth of Knowledge***
U2L10: Comprehension: Author's Purpose	RI.6.6	2

Item 4		
Scoring Rubric	**0 points**	Student does not respond correctly; no response.
	1 point	Answers may vary. Student *either* explains a similarity *or* a difference in the way the authors present information about composting. (See below for sample correct response.)
	2 points	Answers may vary. Sample response: Both authors define and explain the benefits of composting. The author of "Our Compost Journal" presents information through a personal experience, while the author of "Backyard Composting: It's Only Natural" presents information through a persuasive argument that tells why people should compost.

Unit, Lesson, Program Skill	**Common Core State Standard**	**Webb's Depth of Knowledge***
U1L2: Comprehension: Compare Texts	RI.6.9	3

Unit 3 Benchmark Test

Item Number	Correct Answer	Unit, Lesson, Program Skill	Common Core State Standard	Webb's Depth of Knowledge*
		READING AND ANALYZING TEXT		
1	A	U3L12: Comprehension: Story Structure	RL.6.3	1
2	G	U2L6: Comprehension: Understanding Characters	RL.6.3	2
3	A	U2L8: Comprehension: Character's Motivations	RL.6.3	2
4	F	U3L13: Vocabulary Strategy: Figures of Speech	L.6.5a	2
5	A	U3L12: Vocabulary Strategy: Prefixes *en-, ad-*	L.6.4b	2
6	G	U3L14: Comprehension: Theme	RL.6.2	3
7	D	U2L10: Comprehension: Compare and Contrast	RL.6.1	2
8	H	U3L15: Comprehension: Domain-Specific Vocabulary	RI.6.4	2
9	A	U1L5: Comprehension: Author's Purpose	RI.6.6	3
10	F	U3L14: Vocabulary Strategy: Word Relationships	L.6.5b	2
11	C	U3L11: Vocabulary Strategy: Suffixes *-ion, -ation, -ism*	L.6.4b	2
12	G	U3L11: Comprehension: Arguments and Claims	RI.6.8	2
13	A	U2L10: Vocabulary Strategy: Synonyms	L.6.4c	2
14	G	U3L13: Comprehension: Main Ideas and Details	RI.6.2	2
15	C	U3L15: Comprehension: Text and Graphic Features	RI.6.7	2
16	I	U3L13: Comprehension: Main Ideas and Details	RI.6.2	2
17	D	U1L2: Comprehension: Point of View	RI.6.6	2
18	G	U3L12: Comprehension: Story Structure	RL.6.3	2
19	C	U3L9: Comprehension: Cause and Effect	RL.6.3	1
20	F	U3L15: Vocabulary Strategy: Reference Sources	L.6.4c	2
21	C	U2L6: Comprehension: Understanding Characters	RL.6.3	2
22	I	U3L14: Comprehension: Theme	RL.6.2	3
23	A	U1L1: Comprehension: Understanding Characters	RL.6.3	2
24	G	U3L14: Comprehension: Hyperbole	L.6.5a	2
25	A	U1L2: Vocabulary Strategy: Suffixes *-er, -or, -ar, -ist, -ian, -ent*	L.6.4b	2
26	H	U3L12: Comprehension: Story Structure	RL.6.3	1
27	B	U3L14: Comprehension: Author's Word Choice	RL.6.4	3
28	H	U3L11: Comprehension: Figurative Language	RI.6.4	1
29	D	U2L7: Comprehension: Text Structure	RI.6.5	3
30	G	U2L7: Comprehension: Text and Graphic Features	RI.6.7	2

Unit 3 Benchmark Test continued

Item Number	Correct Answer	Unit, Lesson, Program Skill	Common Core State Standard	Webb's Depth of Knowledge*
31	C	U3L13: Comprehension: Domain-Specific Vocabulary	RI.6.4	2
32	H	U3L12: Vocabulary Strategy: Prefixes *en-*, *ad-*	L.6.4b	2
33	A	U3L15: Comprehension: Style and Tone	L.6.3b	3
34	G	U3L13: Comprehension: Compare Texts	RI.6.9	3
35	D	U3L13: Comprehension: Compare Texts	RI.6.9	3
REVISING AND EDITING				
1	A	U3L11: Writing Trait: Word Choice	W.6.5	3
2	G	U1L1: Grammar: Complete Sentences	L.4.1f**	2
3	A	U3L11: Spelling: Suffixes: *-ion* or *-ation*	L.6.2b	1
4	J	U1L4: Grammar: Common and Proper Nouns	L.4.2a**	1
5	D	U1L2: Grammar: Kinds of Sentences	W.6.5	1
6	J	U1L3: Grammar: Subjects and Predicates	L.5.3a**	3
7	A	U3L13: Writing Trait: Organization	W.6.5	3
8	F	U2L7: Grammar: Verbs and Objects	L.6.3a	2
9	D	U3L15: Grammar: Regular and Irregular Verbs	L.3.1d**	1
10	G	U2L6: Grammar: Kinds of Verbs	L.3.1e**	1
11	C	U1L5: Grammar: Other Kinds of Nouns	L.3.1b**	1
12	H	U2L8: Grammar: Coordinating Conjunctions	L.5.1a**	1
13	D	U1L5: Grammar: Other Kinds of Nouns	L.3.1b**	1
14	F	U3L13: Writing Trait: Organization	W.6.5	3
15	C	U2L9: Grammar: Subordinating Conjunctions	L.5.1a**	1
16	G	U3L12: Grammar: Using Pronouns Correctly	L.6.1c	1
17	A	U3L11: Grammar: Subject and Object Pronouns	L.6.1a	1
18	H	U3L14: Spelling: Word Parts *com-*, *con-*	L.6.2b	2
19	A	U2L10: Writing Trait: Sentence Fluency	W.6.5	2
20	G	U2L10: Grammar: Longer Sentences	L.4.2c**	1
WRITING TO EXPLAIN				
	See rubric on page 26.	U3L15: Explanatory Writing	W.6.2a, W.6.2b, W.6.2c, W.6.2d, W.6.2e, W.6.2f	4

** Maintained from previous grade(s).

Unit 3 Reading Complex Text

Item 1		
Scoring Rubric	**0 points**	Student does not respond correctly; no response.
	1 point	Answers may vary. Sample response: Wendy feels gentle concern for Peter because he does not know how to get food in a normal way.

Unit, Lesson, Program Skill	**Common Core State Standard**	**Webb's Depth of Knowledge***
U3L12: Comprehension: Story Structure	RL.6.3	2

Item 2		
Scoring Rubric	**0 points**	Student does not respond correctly; no response.
	1 point	Answers may vary. Sample response: The author describes Neverland as a familiar friend to show that the children feel comfortable with it as soon as they see it.

Unit, Lesson, Program Skill	**Common Core State Standard**	**Webb's Depth of Knowledge***
U3L12: Comprehension: Personification	RL.6.4	2

Item 3		
Scoring Rubric	**0 points**	Student does not respond correctly; no response.
	1 point	Answers may vary. Sample response: The author uses parentheses to show a different point of view, or to tell some new information.

Unit, Lesson, Program Skill	**Common Core State Standard**	**Webb's Depth of Knowledge***
U3L12: Comprehension: Point of View	RL.6.6	3

Item 4		
Scoring Rubric	**0 points**	Student does not respond correctly; no response.
	1 point	Answers may vary. Student correctly describes *either* the characters' experiences of flying in "The Flight" or the boy's experience of flying in "Unflappable Boy." (See below for correct response.)
	2 points	Answers may vary. Sample response: In "The Flight" Peter is a skillful "flyer," while Wendy, John, and Michael are still learning and making mistakes. This contrasts with the poem, where the boy imagines he can fly. He cannot, unlike the characters in "The Flight."

Unit, Lesson, Program Skill	**Common Core State Standard**	**Webb's Depth of Knowledge***
U3L14: Comprehension: Compare Text	RL.6.9	3

Unit 4 Unit Test

Item Number	Correct Answer	Unit, Lesson, Program Skill	Common Core State Standard	Webb's Depth of Knowledge*
		READING AND ANALYZING TEXT		
1	B	U4L20: Comprehension: Main Ideas and Details	RI.6.2	2
2	H	U4L16: Target Vocabulary	L.6.6	1
3	A	U4L18: Decoding: The /sh/ and /zh/ in Final Syllables	RF.5.3a**	1
4	I	U4L18: Vocabulary Strategy: Suffixes -ful, -less, -ly, -ness, -ment, -ship	L.6.4b	2
5	D	U4L16: Comprehension: Compare and Contrast	RI.6.1	2
6	H	U4L17: Comprehension: Fact and Opinion	RI.6.8	2
7	C	U4L17: Decoding: More Common Suffixes	RF.5.3a**	1
8	I	U4L16: Vocabulary Strategy: Greek Roots	L.6.4b	2
9	C	U4L17: Vocabulary Strategy: Word Families	L.6.4b	2
10	I	U4L19: Vocabulary Strategy: Greek Roots and Affixes	L.6.4b	2
11	B	U4L17: Target Vocabulary	L.6.6	1
12	F	U4L16: Comprehension: Compare and Contrast	RI.6.1	2
13	A	U4L20: Comprehension: Main Ideas and Details	RI.6.2	2
14	F	U4L17: Comprehension: Fact and Opinion	RI.6.8	2
15	D	U4L19: Target Vocabulary	L.6.6	1
16	G	U4L20: Comprehension: Main Ideas and Details	RI.6.2	2
17	B	U4L19: Decoding: VV Syllable Pattern	RF.5.3a**	1
18	H	U4L18: Comprehension: Story Structure	RL.6.3	2
19	C	U4L20: Target Vocabulary	L.6.6	1
20	H	U4L17: Vocabulary Strategy: Word Families	L.6.4b	2
21	B	U4L17: Decoding: More Common Suffixes	RF.5.3a**	1
22	I	U4L19: Target Vocabulary	L.6.6	1
23	A	U4L18: Comprehension: Story Structure	RL.6.3	1
24	F	U4L19: Target Vocabulary	L.6.6	1
25	D	U4L19: Vocabulary Strategy: Greek Roots and Affixes	L.6.4b	2
26	H	U4L18: Vocabulary Strategy: Suffixes -ful, -less, -ly, -ness, -ment, -ship	L.6.4b	2
27	C	U4L18: Comprehension: Analyze Setting	RL.6.5	3
28	H	U4L18: Comprehension: Author's Word Choice	RL.6.4	2
29	D	U4L18: Decoding: The /sh/ and /zh/ in Final Syllables	RF.5.3a**	1
30	D	U4L20: Vocabulary Strategy: Prefixes un-, re-, in-, im-, ir-, il-	L.6.4b	2

** Maintained from previous grade(s).

Unit 4 Unit Test continued

Item Number	Correct Answer	Unit, Lesson, Program Skill	Common Core State Standard	Webb's Depth of Knowledge*
31	A	U4L20: Decoding: More Common Prefixes	RF.5.3a**	1
32	F	U4L18: Comprehension: Author's Word Choice	RL.6.4	2
33	B	U4L18: Comprehension: Analyze Setting	RL.6.5	3
34	H	U4L18: Comprehension: Story Structure	RL.6.3	3
35	A	U4L16: Decoding: Comparing Related Words	RF.5.3a**	2
REVISING AND EDITING				
1	C	U4L18: Grammar: Adjectives and Adverbs	L.3.1a**	1
2	H	U4L20: Grammar: Prepositions; Prepositional Phrases	L.4.1e**	1
3	C	U4L19: Grammar: Punctuation	L.6.2a	1
4	H	U4L17: Spelling: Suffixes: *-able/-ible, -ate*	L.6.2b	1
5	B	U4L16: Grammar: Principle Parts of Verbs	L.5.1b**	1
6	I	U4L19: Writing Trait: Organization	W.6.5	3
7	A	U4L17: Grammar: More Kinds of Pronouns	L.6.1b	1
8	H	U4L16: Grammar: Principle Parts of Verbs	L.5.1b**	1
9	B	U4L19: Grammar: Punctuation	L.6.2a	1
10	I	U4L16: Spelling: Suffixes: *-ent, -ant*	L.6.2b	1
11	D	U4L20: Grammar: Prepositions; Prepositional Phrases	L.4.1e**	1
12	F	U4L16: Grammar: Principle Parts of Verbs	L.3.1d**	1
13	C	U4L18: Grammar: Adjectives and Adverbs	L.4.2a**	1
14	I	U4L18: Writing Trait: Sentence Fluency	W.6.5	3
15	D	U4L19: Grammar: Punctuation	L.6.2a	1
16	H	U4L19: Spelling: Plurals	L.6.2b	1
17	C	U4L17: Grammar: More Kinds of Pronouns	L.6.1c	1
18	H	U4L19: Writing Trait: Organization	W.6.5	3
19	A	U4L19: Grammar: Punctuation	L.6.2a	1
20	G	U4L18: Grammar: Adjectives and Adverbs	L.3.1a**	1
WRITING TO INFORM				
See rubric on page 26.		U4L20: Informative Writing	W.6.2a, W.6.2b, W.6.2c, W.6.2d, W.6.2e, W.6.2f	4

** Maintained from previous grade(s).

Unit 4 Reading Complex Text

Item 1		
Scoring Rubric	**0 points**	Student does not respond correctly; no response.
	1 point	Answers may vary. Sample responses: Prometheus is determined to make the world wiser and better, while the other Mighty Folk spend their time eating and drinking. Or, Prometheus decides to live with people and leave the Mighty Folk on the mountaintop.

Unit, Lesson, Program Skill	Common Core State Standard	Webb's Depth of Knowledge*
U4L19: Conclusions and Generalizations	RL.6.1	2

Item 2		
Scoring Rubric	**0 points**	Student does not respond correctly; no response.
	1 point	Answers may vary. Sample responses: Jupiter's refusal to give fire to mankind prompts Prometheus to leave the Mighty Folk and help mankind on his own. Or, it causes mankind to continue to be cold and suffer.

Unit, Lesson, Program Skill	Common Core State Standard	Webb's Depth of Knowledge*
U4L18: Comprehension: Story Structure	RL.6.3	2

Item 3		
Scoring Rubric	**0 points**	Student does not respond correctly; no response.
	1 point	Answers may vary. Sample response: The scene shows how Prometheus sets about resolving the passage's conflict by figuring out, on his own, a way to give fire to mankind.

Unit, Lesson, Program Skill	Common Core State Standard	Webb's Depth of Knowledge*
U3L15: Text Focus: Scenes	RL.6.5	2

Item 4		
Scoring Rubric	**0 points**	Student does not respond correctly; no response.
	1 point	Answers may vary. Student correctly identifies *either* Prometheus's attitude toward mankind *or* the central idea of the passage, but student does not identify both and the connection between them. (See below for sample correct response.)
	2 points	Answers may vary. Sample response: Prometheus's attitude toward mankind is compassionate, generous, and concerned for their welfare. This attitude drives Prometheus to help mankind by bringing them fire, which is the central idea of the passage.

Unit, Lesson, Program Skill	Common Core State Standard	Webb's Depth of Knowledge*
U3L14: Comprehension: Theme	RL.6.2	2

Unit 5 Benchmark Test

Item Number	Correct Answer	Unit, Lesson, Program Skill	Common Core State Standard	Webb's Depth of Knowledge*
		READING AND ANALYZING TEXT		
1	B	U5L24: Comprehension: Author's Purpose	RI.6.6	3
2	I	U5L23: Comprehension: Figurative Language	L.6.5a	3
3	C	U4L20: Comprehension: Main Ideas and Details	RI.6.2	2
4	F	U5L21: Vocabulary Strategy: Word Relationships	L.6.5b	2
5	D	U5L22: Comprehension: Conclusions and Generalizations	RI.6.1	3
6	I	U4L20: Comprehension: Main Ideas and Details	RI.6.2	2
7	B	U5L23: Comprehension: Figurative Language	L.6.5a	2
8	G	U5L23: Comprehension: Understanding Characters	RL.6.3	2
9	B	U5L21: Vocabulary Strategy: Word Relationships	L.6.5b	2
10	F	U4L18: Comprehension: Author's Word Choice	RL.6.4	2
11	A	U4L18: Comprehension: Analyze Setting	RL.6.5	3
12	H	U4L18: Comprehension: Compare Texts	RL.6.9	3
13	D	U4L18: Comprehension: Compare Texts	RL.6.9	3
14	H	U5L23: Vocabulary Strategy: Using Context	L.6.4a	2
15	B	U4L18: Comprehension: Story Structure	RL.6.3	2
16	I	U5L23: Comprehension: Figurative Language	RL.6.4	1
17	D	U5L24: Vocabulary Strategy: Prefixes *con-, com-, pre-, pro-*	L.6.4b	2
18	F	U5L23: Comprehension: Understanding Characters	RL.6.3	2
19	D	U5L21: Comprehension: Point of View	RL.6.6	3
20	G	U5L24: Comprehension: Analyze Events	RI.6.3	2
21	B	U4L16: Vocabulary Strategy: Greek Roots	L.6.4b	2
22	G	U5L22: Comprehension: Text Structure	RI.6.5	3
23	C	U3L15: Comprehension: Text and Graphic Features	RI.6.7	2
24	G	U5L22: Comprehension: Conclusions and Generalizations	RI.6.1	3
25	A	U3L12: Comprehension: Story Structure	RL.6.3	2
26	F	U5L21: Comprehension: Compare and Contrast	RL.6.1	1
27	A	U3L12: Comprehension: Personification	L.6.5a	3
28	G	U5L23: Comprehension: Cause and Effect	RL.6.3	1
29	C	U5L25: Vocabulary Strategy: Suffixes *-able, -ible*	L.6.4b	2
30	G	U5L22: Vocabulary Strategy: Denotation and Connotation	L.6.5c	2
31	C	U3L15: Vocabulary Strategy: Reference Sources	L.6.4c	2
32	G	U5L25: Comprehension: Domain-Specific Vocabulary	RI.6.4	2

Unit 5 Benchmark Test continued

Item Number	Correct Answer	Unit, Lesson, Program Skill	Common Core State Standard	Webb's Depth of Knowledge*
33	B	U4L20: Comprehension: Main Ideas and Details	RI.6.2	2
34	I	U5L22: Comprehension: Conclusions and Generalizations	RI.6.1	2
35	B	U5L25: Comprehension: Sequence of Events	RI.6.5	2
REVISING AND EDITING				
1	A	U1L3: Grammar: Subjects and Predicates	L.5.1a**	2
2	I	U1L2: Grammar: Kinds of Sentences	L.4.3b**	1
3	B	U1L1: Grammar: Complete Sentences	L.4.1f**	2
4	I	U5L21: Spelling: Prefixes *pre-*, *pro-*	L.6.2b	1
5	C	U5L25: Writing Trait: Word Choice	W.6.5	2
6	G	U2L7: Grammar: Verbs and Objects	L.6.3a	2
7	B	U4L19: Writing Trait: Organization	W.6.5	3
8	F	U4L18: Writing Trait: Sentence Fluency	W.6.5	3
9	C	U2L9: Grammar: Subordinating Conjunctions	L.5.2b**	1
10	H	U2L8: Grammar: Coordinating Conjunctions	L.5.1a**	1
11	C	U3L11: Grammar: Subject and Object Pronouns	L.6.1a	1
12	F	U5L22: Spelling: Words with Silent Letters	L.6.2b	1
13	C	U3L14: Grammar: Subject-Verb Agreement	L.3.1f**	1
14	G	U4L16: Grammar: Principal Parts of Verbs	L.5.1b**	1
15	B	U5L23: Spelling: Suffixes: *-ic, -ure, -ous*	L.6.2b	1
16	F	U4L18: Grammar: Adverbs and Adjectives	L.3.1a**	1
17	C	U5L25: Writing Trait: Word Choice	W.6.5	2
18	G	U4L17: Grammar: More Kinds of Pronouns	L.6.1b	1
19	B	U4L18: Grammar: Adjectives and Adverbs	L.4.2a**	1
20	G	U5L22: Grammar: Punctuation and Quotations	L.6.2a	1
21	C	U5L25: Writing Trait: Word Choice	W.6.5	1
22	I	U5L24: Grammar: Making Comparisons	L.3.1g**	1
23	A	U5L25: Grammar: Proper Mechanics	L.5.2b**	1
24	F	U5L21: Grammar: Progressive Forms	L.4.1b**	1
25	B	U4L19: Writing Trait: Organization	W.6.5	3
WRITING ARGUMENTS				
	See rubric on page 24.	U5L25: Argumentative Writing	W.6.1a, W.6.1b, W.6.1c, W.6.1d, W.6.1e	4

** Maintained from previous grade(s).

Unit 5 Reading Complex Text

Item 1		
Scoring Rubric	**0 points**	Student does not respond correctly; no response.
	1 point	Answers may vary. Sample responses: We did not have the technology to learn about Mars. No person or spacecraft had ever visited the planet Mars, and telescopes could not provide images of the planet in great detail.

Unit, Lesson, Program Skill	Common Core State Standard	Webb's Depth of Knowledge*
U5L22: Comprehension: Conclusions and Generalizations	RI.6.1	2

Item 2		
Scoring Rubric	**0 points**	Student does not respond correctly; no response.
	1 point	Answers may vary. Sample response: The author gives examples of past missions to Mars that were becoming increasingly expensive.

Unit, Lesson, Program Skill	Common Core State Standard	Webb's Depth of Knowledge*
U5L24: Comprehension: Analyze Events	RI.6.3	2

Item 3		
Scoring Rubric	**0 points**	Student does not respond correctly; no response.
	1 point	Answers may vary. Sample responses: The author cites several examples of creative solutions that the Sojourner team came up with in developing the rover, such as using a parachute and air bags instead of expensive rockets, using a small solar panel and flashlight batteries instead of large batteries, and using common antennas and motors instead of designing from scratch.

Unit, Lesson, Program Skill	Common Core State Standard	Webb's Depth of Knowledge*
U3L11: Comprehension: Arguments and Claims	RI.6.8	2

Item 4		
Scoring Rubric	**0 points**	Student does not respond correctly; no response.
	1 point	Answers may vary. Student correctly identifies the central idea of the text but does not explain how details about Sojourner and the Pathfinder mission help to convey that idea. (See below for sample correct responses.)
	2 points	Answers may vary. Sample responses: The main idea of the text is that Mars has long been the subject of human speculation, and as science has progressed, so has understanding of Mars. The details about Sojourner and the Pathfinder mission show that humans have made significant strides in understanding and exploring Mars, but still have many unanswered questions. Or, The main idea is that more money does not mean more success. Pathfinder was important because of the high cost, and Sojourner was important because of the low cost. Pathfinder showed that more money didn't help.

Unit, Lesson, Program Skill	Common Core State Standard	Webb's Depth of Knowledge*
U5L25: Comprehension: Main Ideas and Details	RI.6.2	3

Unit 6 Unit Test

Item Number	Correct Answer	Unit, Lesson, Program Skill	Common Core State Standard	Webb's Depth of Knowledge*
		READING AND ANALYZING TEXT		
1	D	U6L28: Comprehension: Understanding Characters	RL.6.3	1
2	G	U6L27: Vocabulary Strategy: Homophones, Homographs, and Homonyms	L.6.4a	1
3	C	U6L30: Vocabulary Strategy: Suffixes -ize, -ify, -ive, -ity	L.6.4b	2
4	F	U6L28: Comprehension: Understanding Characters	RL.6.3	1
5	B	U6L29: Target Vocabulary	L.6.6	1
6	F	U6L26: Decoding: Spelling Patterns in Words from Other Languages	RF.5.3a**	1
7	B	U6L27: Target Vocabulary	L.6.6	1
8	G	U6L28: Comprehension: Understanding Characters	RL.6.3	2
9	C	U6L30: Target Vocabulary	L.6.6	1
10	G	U6L30: Comprehension: Text and Graphic Features	RI.6.7	1
11	C	U6L28: Vocabulary Strategy: Words Often Confused	L.6.4a	1
12	G	U6L26: Vocabulary Strategy: Analogies	L.6.5b	2
13	A	U6L26: Comprehension: Main Ideas and Details	RI.6.2	2
14	I	U6L27: Comprehension: Conclusions and Generalizations	RI.6.1	1
15	C	U6L29: Decoding: Recognizing Prefix Forms	RF.5.3a**	1
16	F	U6L30: Decoding: Confusing Words	RF.5.3a**	1
17	A	U6L26: Comprehension: Main Ideas and Details	RI.6.2	2
18	I	U6L30: Target Vocabulary	L.6.6	1
19	C	U6L26: Comprehension: Main Ideas and Details	RI.6.2	2
20	G	U6L30: Target Vocabulary	L.6.6	1
21	D	U6L29: Vocabulary Strategy: Greek and Latin Roots	L.6.4b	2
22	H	U6L29: Comprehension: Persuasion	RI.6.1	2
23	C	U6L28: Target Vocabulary	L.6.6	1
24	I	U6L27: Comprehension: Conclusions and Generalizations	RI.6.1	2
25	C	U6L27: Vocabulary Strategy: Homophones, Homographs, and Homonyms	L.6.4a	2
26	G	U6L28: Decoding: Recognizing Word Roots	RF.5.3a**	1
27	C	U6L27: Decoding: Recognizing Word Parts	RF.5.3a**	1
28	F	U6L29: Decoding: Recognizing Prefix Forms	RF.5.3a**	1
29	B	U6L29: Comprehension: Persuasion	RI.6.1	2
30	I	U6L27: Comprehension: Conclusions and Generalizations	RI.6.1	2
31	C	U6L30: Vocabulary Strategy: Suffixes -ize, -ify, -ive, -ity	L.6.4b	2
32	F	U6L29: Vocabulary Strategy: Greek and Latin Roots	L.6.4b	2

** Maintained from previous grade(s).

Unit 6 Unit Test continued

Item Number	Correct Answer	Unit, Lesson, Program Skill	Common Core State Standard	Webb's Depth of Knowledge*
33	B	U6L30: Comprehension: Text and Graphic Features	RI.6.7	1
34	H	U6L30: Comprehension: Text and Graphic Features	RI.6.7	1
35	B	U6L30: Decoding: Confusing Words	RF.5.3a**	1
REVISING AND EDITING				
1	B	U6L27: Grammar: More Quotations	L.3.2c**	1
2	I	U6L26: Grammar: Titles and Abbreviations	L.5.2d**	1
3	B	U6L30: Writing Trait: Organization	W.6.5	3
4	I	U6L26: Spelling: Words from Other Languages	L.6.2b	1
5	C	U6L29: Grammar: More Commas	L.4.2c**	1
6	G	U6L28: Grammar: Commas in Sentences	L.5.2b**	1
7	A	U6L30: Grammar: Other Punctuation	L.5.2a**	1
8	G	U6L28: Grammar: Commas in Sentences	L.6.2a	1
9	B	U6L27: Spelling: Greek Word Parts	L.6.2b	1
10	I	U6L26: Writing Trait: Word Choice	W.6.5	3
11	C	U6L29: Grammar: More Commas	L.4.2c**	1
12	G	U6L27: Grammar: More Quotations	L.3.2c**	1
13	B	U6L28: Grammar: Commas in Sentences	L.5.2a**	1
14	F	U6L26: Grammar: Titles and Abbreviations	L.5.2d**	1
15	B	U6L28: Spelling: Latin Word Parts	L.6.2b	1
16	G	U6L29: Grammar: More Commas	L.3.2b**	1
17	C	U6L27: Grammar: More Quotations	L.3.2c**	1
18	F	U6L29: Grammar: More Commas	L.5.2c**	1
19	D	U6L30: Writing Trait: Organization	W.6.2b	3
20	I	U6L30: Spelling: Words Often Confused	L.6.2b	1
21	C	U6L26: Writing Trait: Word Choice	W.6.5	3
22	G	U6L30: Grammar: Other Punctuation	L.5.2a**	1
23	D	U6L27: Grammar: More Quotations	L.3.2c**	1
24	H	U6L30: Grammar: Other Punctuation	L.6.2a	1
25	B	U6L29: Spelling: Greek and Latin Word Parts	L.6.2b	1
WRITING TO NARRATE				
	See rubric on page 28.	U6L30: Narrative Writing	W.6.3a, W.6.3b, W.6.3c, W.6.3d, W.6.3e	4

** Maintained from previous grade(s).

Unit 6 Reading Complex Text

		Item 1
Scoring Rubric	**0 points**	Student does not respond correctly; no response.
	1 point	Answers may vary. Sample response: Christina chooses a banana because it is familiar to her. Student cites all or part of the following: "Though intrigued by these tropical, exotic-looking fruits, I didn't have the faintest notion of how to go about eating them. So instead I grabbed a piece of fruit that I recognized: a banana."

Unit, Lesson, Program Skill	**Common Core State Standard**	**Webb's Depth of Knowledge***
U6L27: Comprehension: Conclusions and Generalizations	RL.6.1	1

		Item 2
Scoring Rubric	**0 points**	Student does not respond correctly; no response.
	1 point	Answers may vary. Sample response: Christina unknowingly bites into a plantain, which she thinks is a banana. This explains the conflict in the passage.

Unit, Lesson, Program Skill	**Common Core State Standard**	**Webb's Depth of Knowledge***
U5L25: Text Focus: Scenes	RL.6.5	2

		Item 3
Scoring Rubric	**0 points**	Student does not respond correctly; no response.
	1 point	Answers may vary. Sample response: Mrs. Lopez means that plantains and bananas belong to the same family, or species, of plant.

Unit, Lesson, Program Skill	**Common Core State Standard**	**Webb's Depth of Knowledge***
U3L12: Comprehension: Personification	RL.6.4	2

		Item 4
Scoring Rubric	**0 points**	Student does not respond correctly; no response.
	1 point	Answers may vary. Student correctly identifies the theme of the passage but does not explain how the narrator's point of view helps to convey that theme. (See below for sample correct responses.)
	2 points	Answers may vary. Sample responses: The theme of the passage is that sharing new foods can be a way of teaching others about different cultures, it is important to be open-minded, or it is important to not judge a book by its cover. By having Christina narrate the passage, the reader gets to understand Christina's experience.

Unit, Lesson, Program Skill	**Common Core State Standard**	**Webb's Depth of Knowledge***
U3L14: Comprehension: Theme	RL.6.2	2

Novel Test

Item Number	Correct Answer	Unit, Lesson, Program Skill	Common Core State Standard	Webb's Depth of Knowledge*
NOVEL TEST: ESPERANZA RISING				
1	C	U4L18: Comprehension: Story Structure	RL.6.3	1
2	H	U4L18: Comprehension: Story Structure	RL.6.3	1
3	C	U6L28: Comprehension: Understanding Characters	RL.6.3	2
4	I	U4L18: Comprehension: Story Structure	RL.6.3	1
5	C	U4L18: Comprehension: Story Structure	RL.6.3	2
6	I	U6L28: Comprehension: Understanding Characters	RL.6.3	2
7	D	U6L28: Comprehension: Understanding Characters	RL.6.3	3
8	H	U4L18: Comprehension: Story Structure	RL.6.3	2
9	C	U4L18: Comprehension: Story Structure	RL.6.3	3
10	F	U6L27: Comprehension: Conclusions and Generalizations	RL.6.1	2
NOVEL TEST: BRIAN'S WINTER				
1	C	U4L18: Comprehension: Story Structure	RL.6.3	1
2	F	U6L28: Comprehension: Understanding Characters	RL.6.3	1
3	C	U5L23: Comprehension: Cause and Effect	RL.6.3	2
4	I	U4L18: Comprehension: Story Structure	RL.6.3	1
5	B	U6L27: Comprehension: Conclusions and Generalizations	RL.6.1	3
6	G	U5L23: Comprehension: Cause and Effect	RL.6.3	2
7	A	U4L18: Comprehension: Story Structure	RL.6.3	1
8	I	U6L28: Comprehension: Understanding Characters	RL.6.3	2
9	C	U5L23: Comprehension: Cause and Effect	RL.6.3	2
10	G	U6L28: Comprehension: Understanding Characters	RL.6.3	3
NOVEL TEST: TRACKING TRASH: FLOTSAM, JETSAM, AND THE SCIENCE OF MOTION				
1	A	U4L17: Comprehension: Fact and Opinion	RI.6.8	2
2	G	U4L19: Comprehension: Cause and Effect	RI.6.1	2
3	D	U6L26: Comprehension: Main Ideas and Details	RI.6.2	1
4	H	U5L24: Comprehension: Author's Purpose	RI.6.6	3
5	D	U6L27: Comprehension: Conclusions and Generalizations	RI.6.1	2
6	F	U6L26: Comprehension: Main Ideas and Details	RI.6.2	2
7	A	U4L17: Comprehension: Fact and Opinion	RI.6.8	2
8	I	U6L26: Comprehension: Main Ideas and Details	RI.6.2	1
9	A	U6L27: Comprehension: Conclusions and Generalizations	RI.6.1	2
10	G	U6L26: Comprehension: Main Ideas and Details	RI.6.2	1

Writing Rubrics

Writing Arguments

Score	Description
6	The writer of this piece • introduces claim(s) and organizes the reasons and evidence clearly. • supports claim(s) with clear reasons and relevant evidence, using credible sources and demonstrating an understanding of the topic or text. • uses words, phrases, and clauses to clarify the relationships among claim(s) and reasons. • establishes and maintains a formal style. • provides a concluding statement or section that follows from the argument presented. • demonstrates exemplary command of the conventions of standard written English.
5	The writer of this piece • introduces claim(s) and mostly organizes the reasons and evidence clearly. • mostly supports claim(s) with clear reasons and relevant evidence, using credible sources and demonstrating an understanding of the topic or text. • uses words, phrases, and clauses to mostly clarify the relationships among claim(s) and reasons. • establishes and maintains a mostly formal style. • provides a concluding statement or section that mostly follows from the argument presented. • demonstrates a good command of the conventions of standard written English.
4	The writer of this piece • introduces claim(s) and mostly organizes the reasons and evidence. • adequately supports claim(s) with reasons and relevant evidence, using credible sources and demonstrating an understanding of the topic or text. • uses words, phrases, and clauses to adequately clarify the relationships among claim(s) and reasons. • establishes and maintains a somewhat formal style. • provides an adequate concluding statement or section that follows from the argument presented. • demonstrates an adequate command of the conventions of standard written English (with occasional errors that do not interfere materially with the underlying message).

Writing Arguments continued

Score	Description
3	The writer of this piece • introduces claim(s) and attempts to organize the reasons and evidence. • supports claim(s) with some reasons and relevant evidence, using credible sources and demonstrating an understanding of the topic or text. • uses some words, phrases, and clauses to clarify the relationships among claim(s) and reasons. • attempts to establish and maintain a formal style. • provides a concluding statement or section that somewhat follows from the argument presented. • demonstrates command of some of the conventions of standard written English (with some errors that do not interfere materially with the underlying message).
2	The writer of this piece • may introduce claim(s); may or may not organize the reasons and evidence. • supports claim(s) with few reasons and relevant evidence. • rarely uses words, phrases, and clauses to clarify the relationships among claim(s) and reasons. • may or may not establish and maintain a formal style. • may provide a concluding statement or section that follows from the argument presented. • demonstrates command of some of the conventions of standard written English (with some errors that may interfere materially with the underlying message).
1	The writer of this piece • may attempt to introduce claim(s); may or may not organize the reasons and evidence. • supports claim(s) with few, if any, reasons and relevant evidence. • does not use words, phrases, and clauses to clarify the relationships among claim(s) and reasons. • does not establish and maintain a formal style. • may or may not provide a concluding statement or section that follows from the argument presented. • demonstrates little or no command of the conventions of standard written English.

Writing to Inform/Explain

Score	Description
6	The writer of this piece • introduces a topic; organizes ideas, concepts, and information, using strategies such as definition, classification, comparison/contrast, and cause/effect; includes formatting, graphics, and multimedia when useful to aiding comprehension. • develops the topic with relevant facts, definitions, concrete details, quotations, or other information and examples. • uses appropriate transitions to clarify the relationships among ideas and concepts. • uses precise language and domain-specific vocabulary to inform about or explain the topic. • establishes and maintains a formal style. • provides a concluding statement or section that follows from the information or explanation presented. • demonstrates exemplary command of the conventions of standard written English.
5	The writer of this piece • introduces a topic; mostly organizes ideas, concepts, and information, using strategies such as definition, classification, comparison/contrast, and cause/effect; includes formatting, graphics, and multimedia when useful to aiding comprehension. • mostly develops the topic with relevant facts, definitions, concrete details, quotations, or other information and examples. • uses mostly appropriate transitions to clarify the relationships among ideas and concepts. • uses mostly precise language and domain-specific vocabulary to inform about or explain the topic. • establishes and maintains a mostly formal style. • provides a concluding statement or section that mostly follows from the information or explanation presented. • demonstrates a good command of the conventions of standard written English.
4	The writer of this piece • introduces a topic adequately; mostly organizes ideas, concepts, and information, using strategies such as definition, classification, comparison/contrast, and cause/effect; includes some formatting, graphics, and multimedia when useful to aiding comprehension. • adequately develops the topic with relevant facts, definitions, concrete details, quotations, or other information and examples. • uses adequate transitions to clarify the relationships among ideas and concepts. • adequately uses precise language and domain-specific vocabulary to inform about or explain the topic. • establishes and maintains a somewhat formal style. • provides an adequate concluding statement or section that follows from the information or explanation presented. • demonstrates an adequate command of the conventions of standard written English (with occasional errors that do not interfere materially with the underlying message).

Writing to Inform/Explain continued

Score	Description
3	The writer of this piece • introduces a topic; sometimes organizes ideas, concepts, and information, using strategies such as definition, classification, comparison/contrast, and cause/effect; may include some formatting, graphics, and multimedia when useful to aiding comprehension. • develops the topic with some relevant facts, definitions, concrete details, quotations, or other information and examples. • uses some transitions to mostly clarify the relationships among ideas and concepts. • may use some precise language and domain-specific vocabulary to inform about or explain the topic. • attempts to establish and maintain a formal style. • provides a concluding statement or section that somewhat follows from the information or explanation presented. • demonstrates command of some of the conventions of standard written English (with some errors that do not interfere materially with the underlying message).
2	The writer of this piece • may introduce a topic; may organize ideas, concepts, and information, using strategies such as definition, classification, comparison/contrast, and cause/effect; may or may not include formatting, graphics, and multimedia when useful to aiding comprehension. • briefly develops the topic with few relevant facts, definitions, concrete details, quotations, or other information and examples. • attempts to use transitions to clarify the relationships among ideas and concepts. • rarely uses precise language and domain-specific vocabulary to inform about or explain the topic. • may or may not establish and maintain a formal style. • may provide a concluding statement or section that follows from the information or explanation presented. • demonstrates command of some of the conventions of standard written English (with some errors that may interfere materially with the underlying message).
1	The writer of this piece • may attempt to introduce a topic; may or may not organize ideas, concepts, and information, using strategies such as definition, classification, comparison/contrast, and cause/effect; includes little or no formatting, graphics, and multimedia when useful to aiding comprehension. • develops the topic with few, if any, facts, definitions, concrete details, quotations, or other information and examples. • may or may not use transitions to clarify the relationships among ideas and concepts. • does not use precise language and domain-specific vocabulary to inform about or explain the topic. • does not establish and maintain a formal style. • may or may not provide a concluding statement or section that follows from the information or explanation presented. • demonstrates little or no command of the conventions of standard written English.

Writing to Narrate

Score	Description
6	The writer of this piece • engages and orients the reader by establishing a context and introducing a narrator and/or characters; organizes an event sequence that unfolds naturally and logically. • uses narrative techniques, such as dialogue, pacing, and description, to develop experiences, events, and/or characters. • uses a variety of transitional words, phrases, and clauses to convey sequence and signal shifts from one time frame or setting to another. • uses precise words and phrases, relevant descriptive details, and sensory language to convey experiences and events. • provides a conclusion that follows from the narrated experiences or events. • demonstrates exemplary command of the conventions of standard written English.
5	The writer of this piece • engages and orients the reader by establishing a context and introducing a narrator and/or characters; mostly organizes an event sequence that unfolds naturally and logically. • mostly uses narrative techniques, such as dialogue, pacing, and description, to develop experiences, events, and/or characters. • uses a variety of transitional words, phrases, and clauses to mostly convey sequence and signal shifts from one time frame or setting to another. • uses precise words and phrases, relevant descriptive details, and sensory language to mostly convey experiences and events. • provides a conclusion that mostly follows from the narrated experiences or events. • demonstrates a good command of the conventions of standard written English.
4	The writer of this piece • adequately engages and orients the reader by establishing a context and introducing a narrator and/or characters; mostly organizes an event sequence that unfolds naturally and logically. • adequately uses narrative techniques, such as dialogue, pacing, and description, to develop experiences, events, and/or characters. • uses an adequate variety of transitional words, phrases, and clauses to convey sequence and signal shifts from one time frame or setting to another. • uses precise words and phrases, relevant descriptive details, and sensory language to adequately convey experiences and events. • provides an adequate conclusion that follows from the narrated experiences or events. • demonstrates an adequate command of the conventions of standard written English (with occasional errors that do not interfere materially with the underlying message).

Writing to Narrate continued

Score	Description
3	The writer of this piece • engages and orients the reader by establishing a context and introducing a narrator and/or characters; attempts to organize an event sequence that unfolds naturally and logically. • uses some narrative techniques, such as dialogue, pacing, and description, to develop experiences, events, and/or characters. • uses some transitional words, phrases, and clauses to convey sequence and signal shifts from one time frame or setting to another. • may use some precise words and phrases, relevant descriptive details, and sensory language to convey experiences and events. • provides a conclusion that somewhat follows from the narrated experiences or events. • demonstrates command of some of the conventions of standard written English (with some errors that do not interfere materially with the underlying message).
2	The writer of this piece • may engage and orient the reader by establishing a context and introducing a narrator and/or characters; may or may not organize an event sequence. • uses few narrative techniques, such as dialogue, pacing, and description, to develop experiences, events, and/or characters. • attempts to use transitional words, phrases, and clauses to convey sequence and signal shifts from one time frame or setting to another. • rarely uses precise words and phrases, relevant descriptive details, and sensory language to convey experiences and events. • may provide a conclusion that follows from the narrated experiences or events. • demonstrates command of some of the conventions of standard written English (with some errors that may interfere materially with the underlying message).
1	The writer of this piece • may attempt to engage and orient the reader by establishing a context and introducing a narrator and/or characters; may or may not organize an event sequence. • uses few or no narrative techniques, such as dialogue, pacing, and description, to develop experiences, events, and/or characters. • uses few, if any, transitional words, phrases, and clauses to convey sequence and signal shifts from one time frame or setting to another. • does not use precise words and phrases, relevant descriptive details, and sensory language to convey experiences and events. • may or may not provide a conclusion that follows from the narrated experiences or events. • demonstrates little or no command of the conventions of standard written English.

Answer Document

This answer sheet has three sections. Remember to use the correct section!

There may be more answer rows than you need. Before you begin a section, see how many questions are in it. Then draw a line on this form under the last row you will need, to show where you will stop.

Reading and Analyzing Text

1. Ⓐ Ⓑ Ⓒ Ⓓ
2. Ⓕ Ⓖ Ⓗ Ⓘ
3. Ⓐ Ⓑ Ⓒ Ⓓ
4. Ⓕ Ⓖ Ⓗ Ⓘ
5. Ⓐ Ⓑ Ⓒ Ⓓ
6. Ⓕ Ⓖ Ⓗ Ⓘ
7. Ⓐ Ⓑ Ⓒ Ⓓ
8. Ⓕ Ⓖ Ⓗ Ⓘ
9. Ⓐ Ⓑ Ⓒ Ⓓ
10. Ⓕ Ⓖ Ⓗ Ⓘ
11. Ⓐ Ⓑ Ⓒ Ⓓ
12. Ⓕ Ⓖ Ⓗ Ⓘ
13. Ⓐ Ⓑ Ⓒ Ⓓ
14. Ⓕ Ⓖ Ⓗ Ⓘ
15. Ⓐ Ⓑ Ⓒ Ⓓ
16. Ⓕ Ⓖ Ⓗ Ⓘ
17. Ⓐ Ⓑ Ⓒ Ⓓ
18. Ⓕ Ⓖ Ⓗ Ⓘ
19. Ⓐ Ⓑ Ⓒ Ⓓ
20. Ⓕ Ⓖ Ⓗ Ⓘ
21. Ⓐ Ⓑ Ⓒ Ⓓ
22. Ⓕ Ⓖ Ⓗ Ⓘ
23. Ⓐ Ⓑ Ⓒ Ⓓ
24. Ⓕ Ⓖ Ⓗ Ⓘ

25. Ⓐ Ⓑ Ⓒ Ⓓ
26. Ⓕ Ⓖ Ⓗ Ⓘ
27. Ⓐ Ⓑ Ⓒ Ⓓ
28. Ⓕ Ⓖ Ⓗ Ⓘ
29. Ⓐ Ⓑ Ⓒ Ⓓ
30. Ⓕ Ⓖ Ⓗ Ⓘ
31. Ⓐ Ⓑ Ⓒ Ⓓ
32. Ⓕ Ⓖ Ⓗ Ⓘ
33. Ⓐ Ⓑ Ⓒ Ⓓ
34. Ⓕ Ⓖ Ⓗ Ⓘ
35. Ⓐ Ⓑ Ⓒ Ⓓ

Revising and Editing

1. Ⓐ Ⓑ Ⓒ Ⓓ
2. Ⓕ Ⓖ Ⓗ Ⓘ
3. Ⓐ Ⓑ Ⓒ Ⓓ
4. Ⓕ Ⓖ Ⓗ Ⓘ
5. Ⓐ Ⓑ Ⓒ Ⓓ
6. Ⓕ Ⓖ Ⓗ Ⓘ
7. Ⓐ Ⓑ Ⓒ Ⓓ
8. Ⓕ Ⓖ Ⓗ Ⓘ
9. Ⓐ Ⓑ Ⓒ Ⓓ
10. Ⓕ Ⓖ Ⓗ Ⓘ
11. Ⓐ Ⓑ Ⓒ Ⓓ
12. Ⓕ Ⓖ Ⓗ Ⓘ

13. Ⓐ Ⓑ Ⓒ Ⓓ
14. Ⓕ Ⓖ Ⓗ Ⓘ
15. Ⓐ Ⓑ Ⓒ Ⓓ
16. Ⓕ Ⓖ Ⓗ Ⓘ
17. Ⓐ Ⓑ Ⓒ Ⓓ
18. Ⓕ Ⓖ Ⓗ Ⓘ
19. Ⓐ Ⓑ Ⓒ Ⓓ
20. Ⓕ Ⓖ Ⓗ Ⓘ
21. Ⓐ Ⓑ Ⓒ Ⓓ
22. Ⓕ Ⓖ Ⓗ Ⓘ
23. Ⓐ Ⓑ Ⓒ Ⓓ
24. Ⓕ Ⓖ Ⓗ Ⓘ
25. Ⓐ Ⓑ Ⓒ Ⓓ

Unit 6 Novel Test

Title: _____

1. Ⓐ Ⓑ Ⓒ Ⓓ
2. Ⓕ Ⓖ Ⓗ Ⓘ
3. Ⓐ Ⓑ Ⓒ Ⓓ
4. Ⓕ Ⓖ Ⓗ Ⓘ
5. Ⓐ Ⓑ Ⓒ Ⓓ
6. Ⓕ Ⓖ Ⓗ Ⓘ
7. Ⓐ Ⓑ Ⓒ Ⓓ
8. Ⓕ Ⓖ Ⓗ Ⓘ
9. Ⓐ Ⓑ Ⓒ Ⓓ
10. Ⓕ Ⓖ Ⓗ Ⓘ

Student Name _____

Test Record Form

See the Answer Key for item analysis, including specific skills tested. For struggling children, use the Performance Summary to determine skills for reteaching.

Unit 1 Benchmark Test Date Administered _____	Possible Score	Acceptable Score	Student Score	Percent Correct (%) (Optional)
Reading and Analyzing Text	35	25		Student Score × 2.86 = %
Revising and Editing	20	14		Student Score × 5 = %
Writing to Narrate	6	4		
Reading Complex Text	5	3		

Unit 2 Unit Test Date Administered _____	Possible Score	Acceptable Score	Student Score	Percent Correct (%) (Optional)
Reading and Analyzing Text	35	25		Student Score × 2.86 = %
Revising and Editing	20	14		Student Score × 5 = %
Writing Arguments	6	4		
Reading Complex Text	5	3		

Unit 3 Benchmark Test Date Administered _____	Possible Score	Acceptable Score	Student Score	Percent Correct (%) (Optional)
Reading and Analyzing Text	35	25		Student Score × 2.86 = %
Revising and Editing	20	14		Student Score × 5 = %
Writing to Explain	6	4		
Reading Complex Text	5	3		

Test Record Form
31
Grade 6 Benchmark and Unit Tests
Teacher's Edition

Student Name _____

Test Record Form continued

Unit 4 Unit Test Date Administered _____	Possible Score	Acceptable Score	Student Score	Percent Correct (%) (Optional)
Reading and Analyzing Text	35	25		Student Score × 2.86 = %
Revising and Editing	20	14		Student Score × 5 = %
Writing to Inform	6	4		
Reading Complex Text	5	3		

Unit 5 Benchmark Test Date Administered _____	Possible Score	Acceptable Score	Student Score	Percent Correct (%) (Optional)
Reading and Analyzing Text	35	25		Student Score × 2.86 = %
Revising and Editing	25	17		Student Score × 4 = %
Writing Arguments	6	4		
Reading Complex Text	5	3		

Unit 6 Unit Test Date Administered _____	Possible Score	Acceptable Score	Student Score	Percent Correct (%) (Optional)
Reading and Analyzing Text	35	25		Student Score × 2.86 = %
Revising and Editing	25	17		Student Score × 4 = %
Writing to Narrate	6	4		
Reading Complex Text	5	3		

Unit 6 Novel Test Date Administered _____	Possible Score	Acceptable Score	Student Score	Percent Correct (%) (Optional)
Novel Test	10	8		Student Score × 10 = %

Student Name _____

Performance Summary

For struggling students, copy this form and circle the items answered incorrectly. In the third column record the specific skills for reteaching, using the item analysis on the Answer Key.

Unit 1 Benchmark Test   Date Administered _____

Reading Skills Performance		
Skill	**Items**	**Skills for Reteaching**
Comprehension Skills	1, 4, 5, 6, 7, 10, 11, 12, 13, 14, 15, 17, 18, 19, 20, 21, 23, 24, 26, 27, 28, 29, 30, 31, 32, 34, 35	
Vocabulary Strategies	2, 3, 8, 9, 16, 22, 25, 33	

Writing and Grammar Skills Performance		
Skill	**Items**	**Skills for Reteaching**
Writing Traits	1, 2, 12, 20	
Grammar	4, 5, 6, 7, 8, 9, 10, 11, 13, 15, 16, 17, 18, 19	
Spelling	3, 14	
Writing Form	Writing Prompt	

Unit 2 Unit Test   Date Administered _____

Reading Skills Performance		
Skill	**Items**	**Skills for Reteaching**
Comprehension Skills	5, 9, 11, 13, 15, 16, 17, 18, 24, 28, 31, 32, 34, 35	
Target Vocabulary	1, 4, 12, 19, 29, 33	
Vocabulary Strategies	2, 6, 8, 10, 20, 25, 26, 27	
Decoding	3, 7, 14, 21, 22, 23, 30	

Writing and Grammar Skills Performance		
Skill	**Items**	**Skills for Reteaching**
Writing Traits	1, 12, 15	
Grammar	2, 3, 5, 6, 7, 8, 9, 11, 13, 14, 16, 17, 18, 19	
Spelling	4, 10, 20	
Writing Form	Writing Prompt	

Unit 3 Benchmark Test   Date Administered _____

Reading Skills Performance		
Skill	**Items**	**Skills for Reteaching**
Comprehension Skills	1, 2, 3, 6, 7, 8, 9, 12, 14, 15, 16, 17, 18, 19, 21, 22, 23, 24, 26, 27, 28, 29, 30, 31, 33, 34, 35	
Vocabulary Strategies	4, 5, 10, 11, 13, 20, 25, 32	

Writing and Grammar Skills Performance		
Skill	**Items**	**Skills for Reteaching**
Writing Traits	1, 7, 14, 19	
Grammar	2, 4, 5, 6, 8, 9, 10, 11, 12, 13, 15, 16, 17, 20	
Spelling	3, 18	
Writing Form	Writing Prompt	

Performance Summary continued

Unit 4 Unit Test   Date Administered _____

Reading Skills Performance		
Skill	**Items**	**Skills for Reteaching**
Comprehension Skills	1, 5, 6, 12, 13, 14, 16, 18, 23, 27, 28, 32, 33, 34	
Target Vocabulary	2, 11, 15, 19, 22, 24	
Vocabulary Strategies	4, 8, 9, 10, 20, 25, 26, 30	
Decoding	3, 7, 17, 21, 29, 31, 35	

Writing and Grammar Skills Performance		
Skill	**Items**	**Skills for Reteaching**
Writing Traits	6, 14, 18	
Grammar	1, 2, 3, 5, 7, 8, 9, 11, 12, 13, 15, 17, 19, 20	
Spelling	4, 10, 16	
Writing Form	Writing Prompt	

Unit 5 Benchmark Test   Date Administered _____

Reading Skills Performance		
Skill	**Items**	**Skills for Reteaching**
Comprehension Skills	1, 2, 3, 5, 6, 7, 8, 10, 11, 12, 13, 15, 16, 18, 19, 20, 22, 23, 24, 25, 26, 27, 28, 32, 33, 34, 35	
Vocabulary Strategies	4, 9, 14, 17, 21, 29, 30, 31	

Writing and Grammar Skills Performance		
Skill	**Items**	**Skills for Reteaching**
Writing Traits	5, 7, 8, 17, 21, 25	
Grammar	1, 2, 3, 6, 9, 10, 11, 13, 14, 16, 18, 19, 20, 22, 23, 24	
Spelling	4, 12, 15	
Writing Form	Writing Prompt	

Unit 6 Unit Test   Date Administered _____

Reading Skills Performance		
Skill	**Items**	**Skills for Reteaching**
Comprehension Skills	1, 4, 8, 10, 13, 14, 17, 19, 22, 24, 29, 30, 33, 34	
Target Vocabulary	5, 7, 9, 18, 20, 23	
Vocabulary Strategies	2, 3, 11, 12, 21, 25, 31, 32	
Decoding	6, 15, 16, 26, 27, 28, 35	

Writing and Grammar Skills Performance		
Skill	**Items**	**Skills for Reteaching**
Writing Traits	3, 10, 19, 21	
Grammar	1, 2, 5, 6, 7, 8, 11, 12, 13, 14, 16, 17, 18, 22, 23, 24	
Spelling	4, 9, 15, 20, 25	
Writing Form	Writing Prompt	